Richard Ashcroft
Human Conditions

Piano, vocal & guitar tablature

www.richardashcroft.com

Check The Meaning

Richard Ashcroft: Vocals, Guitars and Bass.
Pete Salisbury: Drums.
Kate Radley: Keyboards.
Martyn Campbell: Bass.
Talvin Singh: Duggi Tarang, Shruti Box & Madal.
Chuck Leavell: Piano.
Richard Robson: Programming.
Steve Sidelnyk: Drum programming.

Buy It In Bottles

Richard Ashcroft: Vocals, Guitars & Percussion.
Pete Salisbury: Drums.
Martyn Campbell: Bass.
Craig Wagstaff: Percussion.
Chuck Leavell: Piano.
Richard Robson: Programming.
Steve Sidelnyk: Drum programming.

Bright Lights

Richard Ashcroft: Vocals, Guitars & Piano.
Pete Salisbury: Drums.
Martyn Campbell: Bass.
Talvin Singh: Tablas.
Richard Robson: Programming.
Steve Sidelnyk: Drum programming.

Paradise

Richard Ashcroft: Vocals, Guitars.
Pete Salisbury: Drums.
Kate Radley: Keyboards.
Martyn Campbell: Bass.
Craig Wagstaff: Percussion.
Richard Robson: Programming.
Steve Sidelnyk: Programming.

God In The Numbers

Richard Ashcroft: Vocals, Guitars, Keyboards & Percussion.
Pete Salisbury: Drums.
Kate Radley: Keyboards.
Martyn Campbell: Bass.
Craig Wagstaff: Percussion.
Jim Hunt: Flute.
Richard Robson: Programming.
Steve Sidelnyk: Drum programming.

Science Of Silence

Richard Ashcroft: Vocals, Guitars, Percussion & Wurlitzer.
Pete Salisbury: Drums.
Martyn Campbell: Bass.
Richard Robson: Programming.
Steve Sidelnyk: Drum Programming.

Man On A Mission

Richard Ashcroft: Vocals, Guitars, Bass & Percussion.
Pete Salisbury: Drums.
Martyn Campbell: Bass.
Richard Robson: Programming.
Steve Sidelnyk: Drum programming.

Running Away

Richard Ashcroft: Vocals, Guitars, Bass & Piano.
Pete Salisbury: Drums.
Martyn Campbell: Bass.
Talvin Singh: Beats & Drones.
Jim Hunt: Saxaphone.
Matt Clifford: Wurlitzer.
Richard Robson: Programming.
Steve Sidelnyk: Drum programming.

Lord I've Been Trying

Richard Ashcroft: Vocals & Guitars.
Pete Salisbury: Drums.
Kate Radley: Keyboards.
Martyn Campbell: Bass.
Chuck Leavell: Hammond organ & Piano.
Craig Wagstaff: Percussion.
Richard Robson: Programming.
Steve Sidelnyk: Drum programming.

Nature Is The Law

Richard Ashcroft: Vocals, Guitars, Bass & Percussion.
Pete Salisbury: Drums.
Martyn Campbell: Bass.
Talvin Singh: Tablas.
Jim Hunt: Flute.
Richard Robson: Programming.
Steve Sidelnyk: Drum programming.
Backing vocals arranged and performed by Brian Wilson.

The Miracle

Richard Ashcroft : Vocals, Guitars, Keyboards & Percussion.
Pete Salisbury : Drums.
Martyn Campbell : Bass.
Richard Robson : Programming.
Steve Sidelnyk : Percussion & Drum Programming.
Strings by London Session Orchestra led by Gavin Wright.
Choir : London Community Gospel Choir.

Orchestra arranged and conducted by Wil Malone

Published 2002
© International Music Publications Limited
Griffin house, 161 Hammersmith Road, London, W6 8BS, England.
All tracks written by Richard Ashcroft.
Published by EMI Music Publishing Ltd.
Management : Marc Marot, assisted by Bob Young
for Terra Firma Management Ltd.
Editor : Chris Harvey.
Music arrangement : Artemis Music Ltd.
Original artwork : Love.
Photography : Nadav Kandar, Max Dodson and Marc Marot.
Folio design : Dominic Brookman.

got my mind meditating on love, love

Check The Meaning

Words and Music by Richard Ashcroft

Buy It In Bottles

Words and Music by Richard Ashcroft

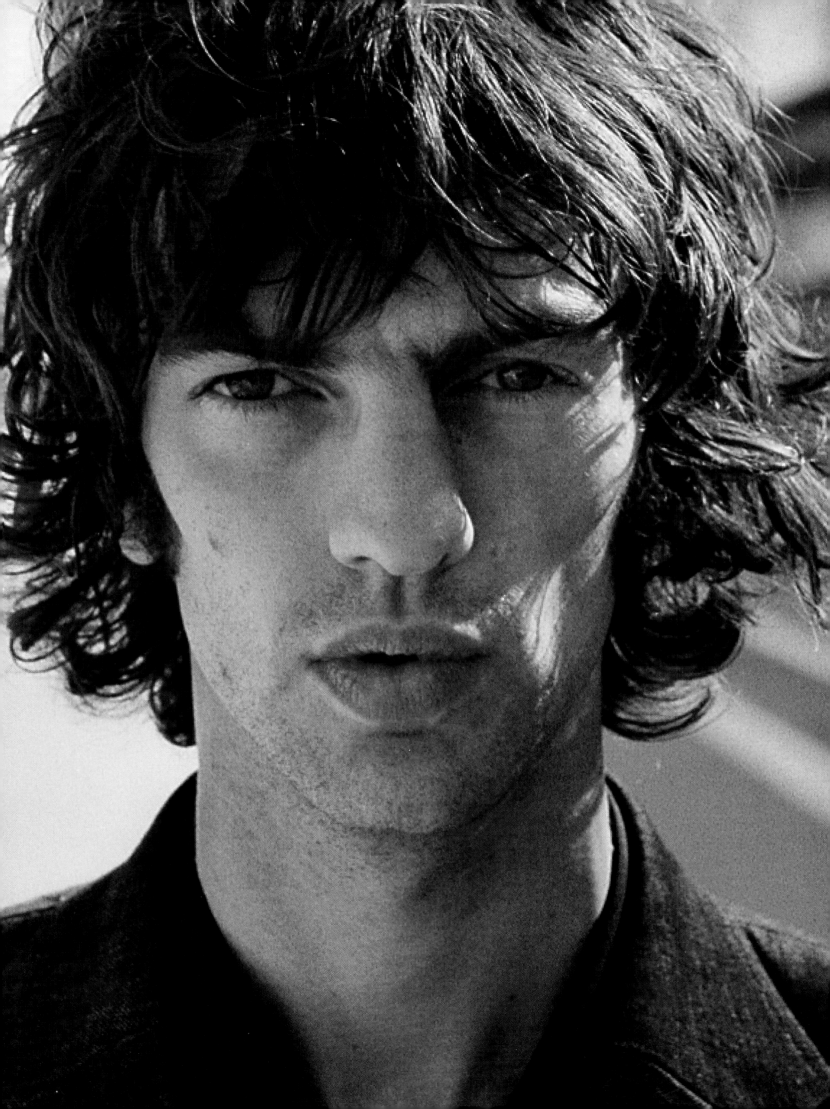

Bright Lights

Words and Music by Richard Ashcroft

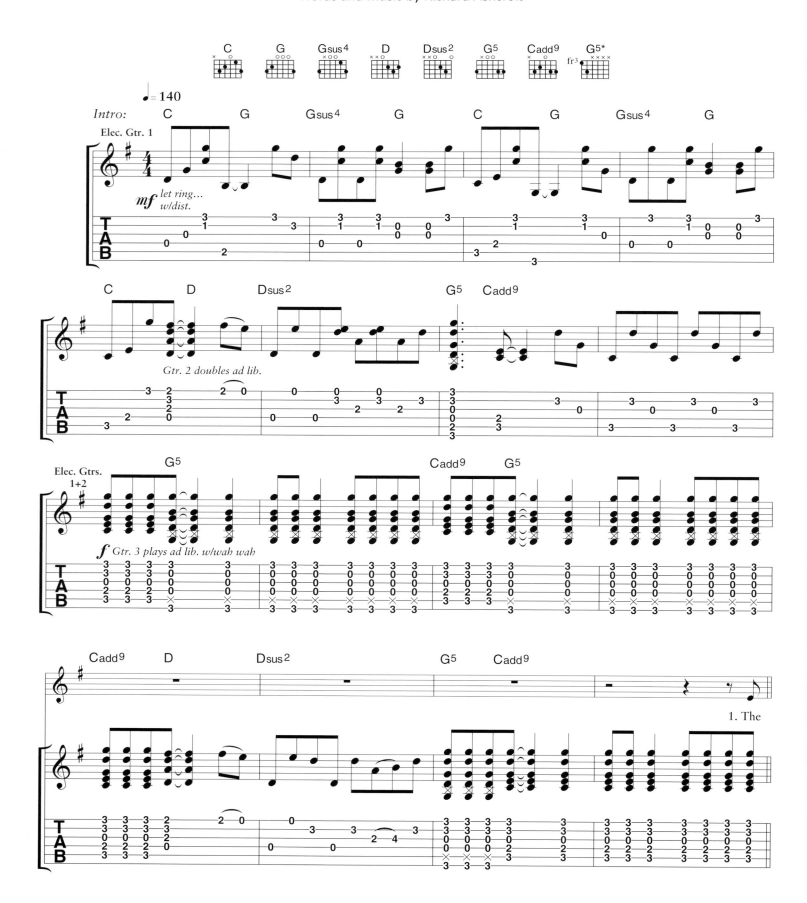

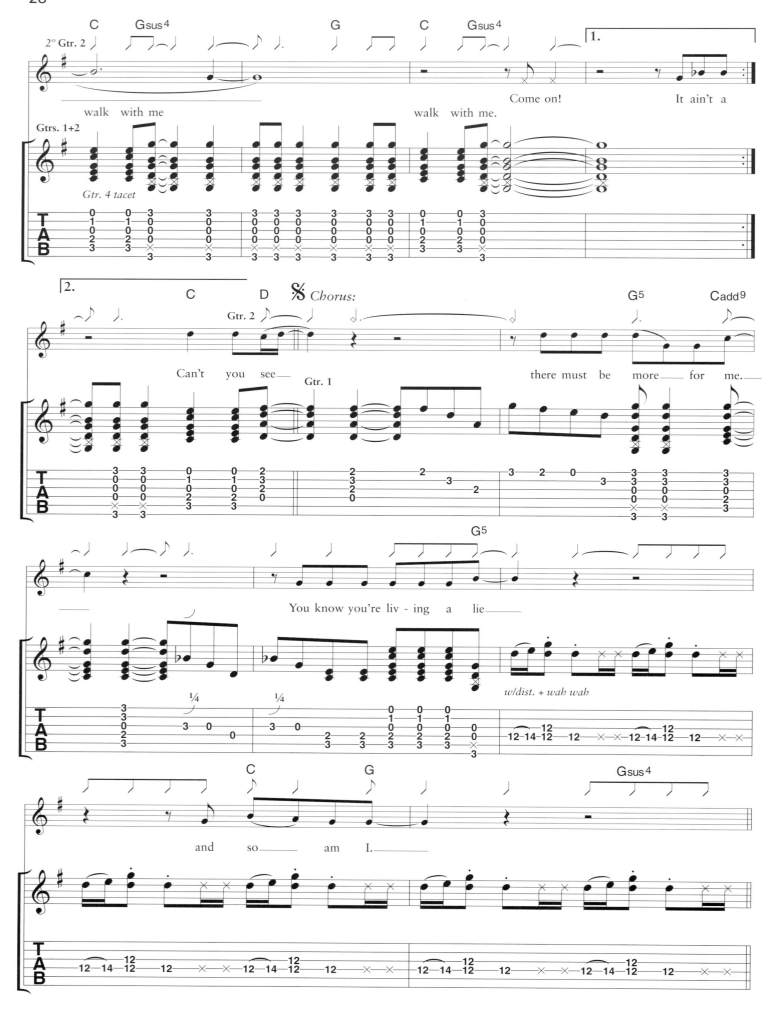

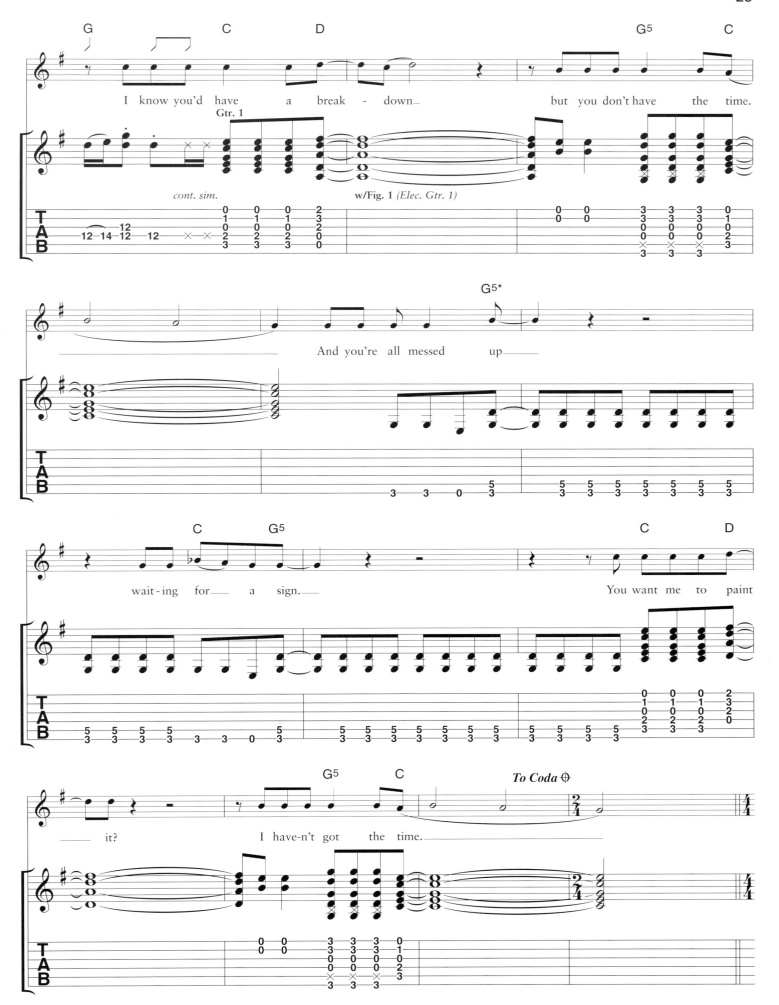

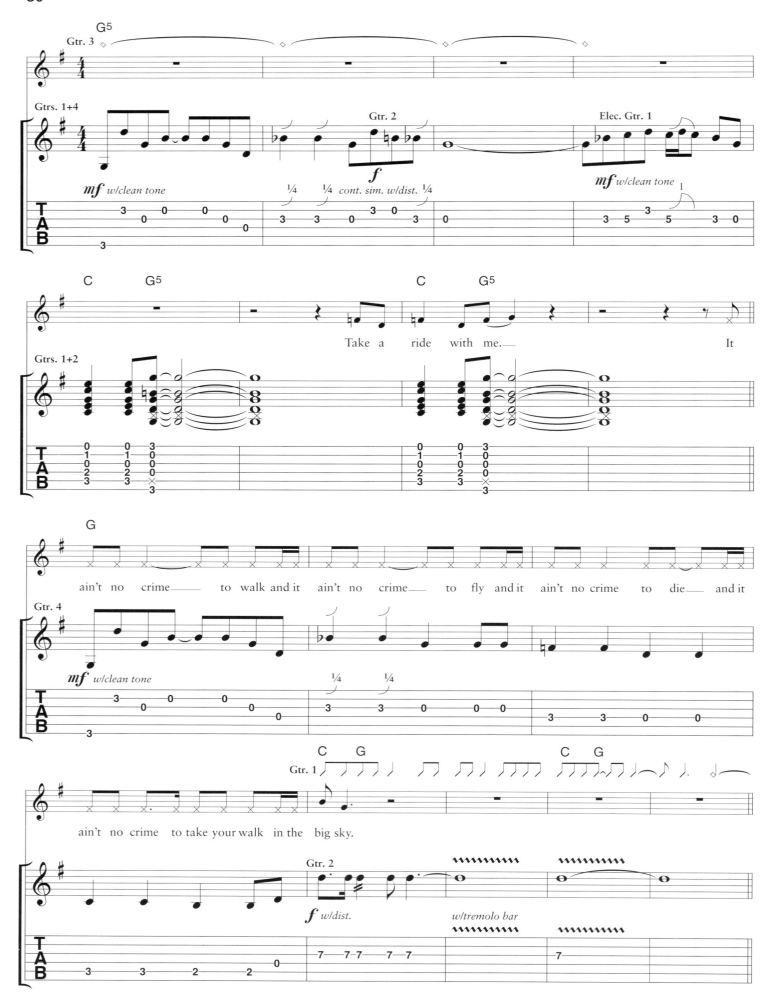

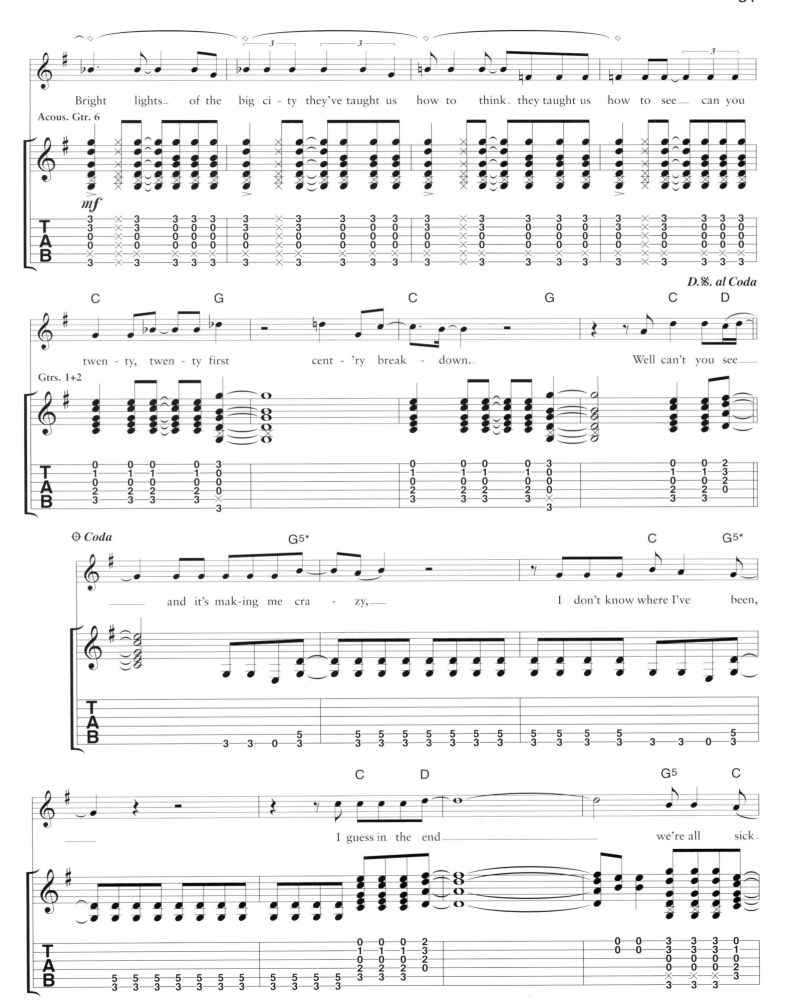

Paradise

Words and Music by Richard Ashcroft

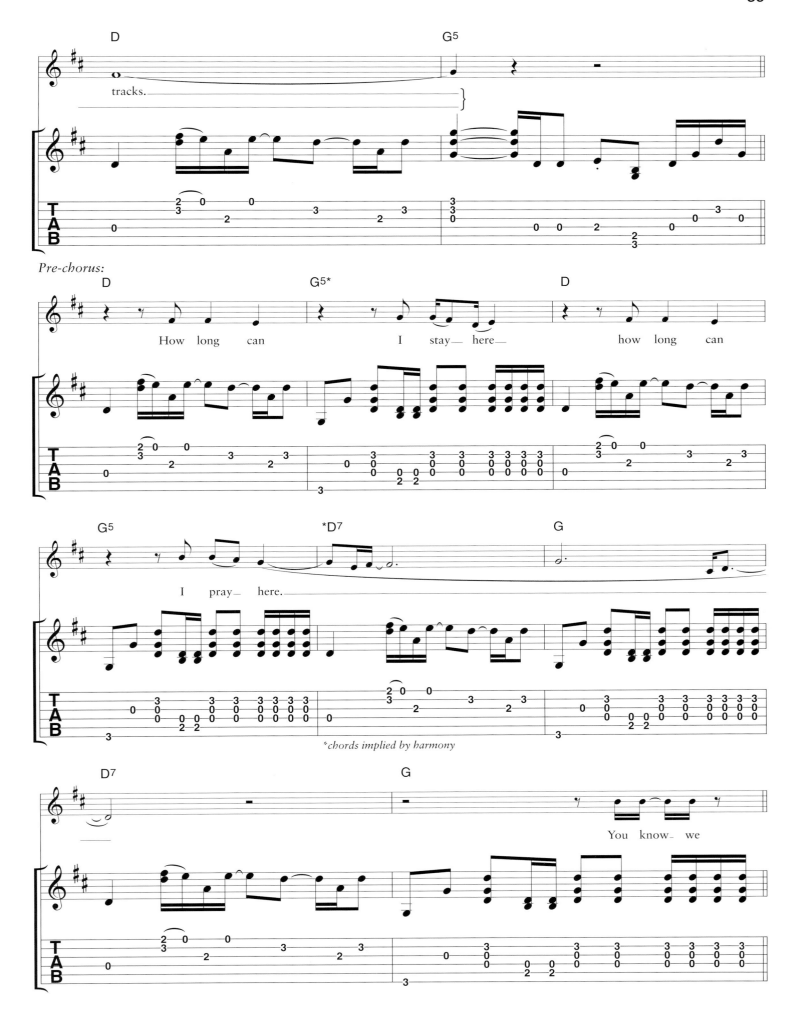

We'll leave in the morn-ing.

We'll leave in the morn-ing.

God In The Numbers

Words and Music by Richard Ashcroft

Verse 3:
I know that I could learn a little harder
There's so much that I want to read and know
But maybe I'm a little lazy
Maybe I don't really want to know.

I saw God in the numbers *etc.*

Verse 4:
The more I learn of history the more I hate it
'Cause we're repeating things we did a thousand years ago
We're building palaces of fortune in the sky
There's an underclass dying whilst we smile.

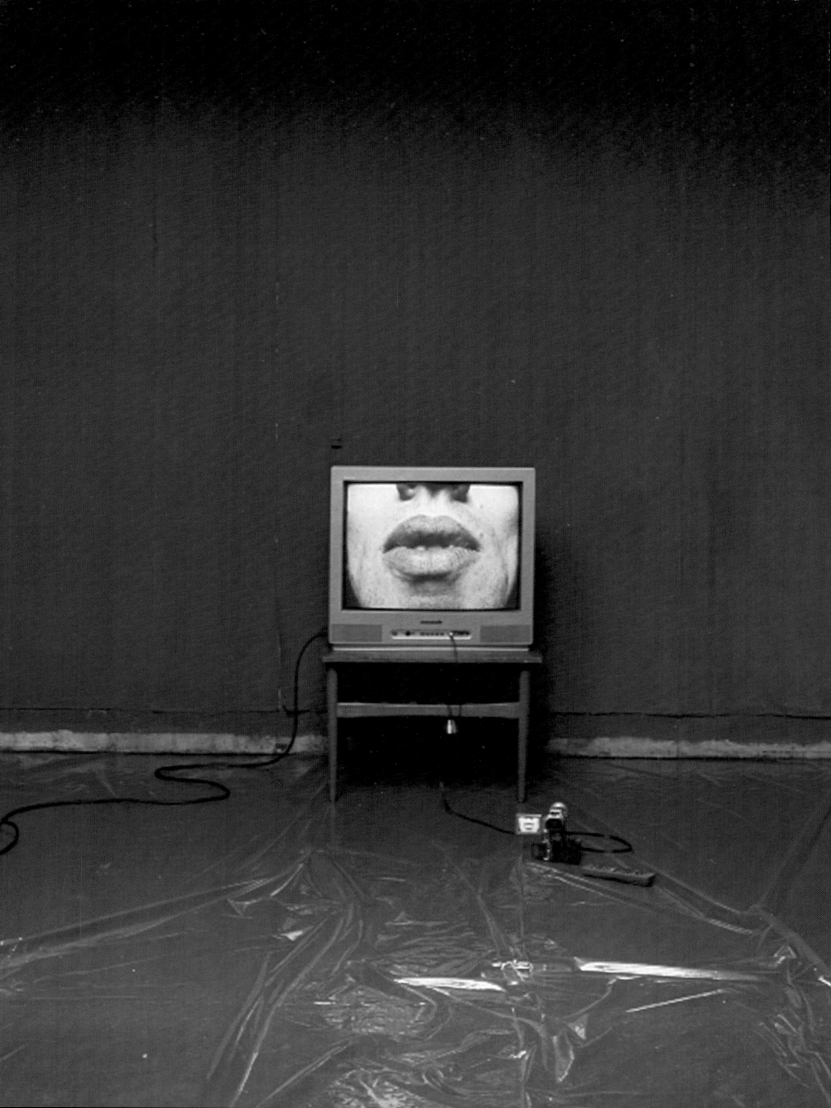

Science Of Silence

Words and Music by Richard Ashcroft

Fade out:
(We are on a rock, spinning in infinity)
Oh I see so much joy and it makes me scared
(We are on a rock, spinning silently)
Oh I don't know if my prayers are received, until the end
(We are on a rock, spinning in infinity)
Oh I guess it ain't often for you to pray for peace
Oh baby, I don't know where I'm going
All I know is that I need you as a friend.

Man On A Mission

Words and Music by Richard Ashcroft

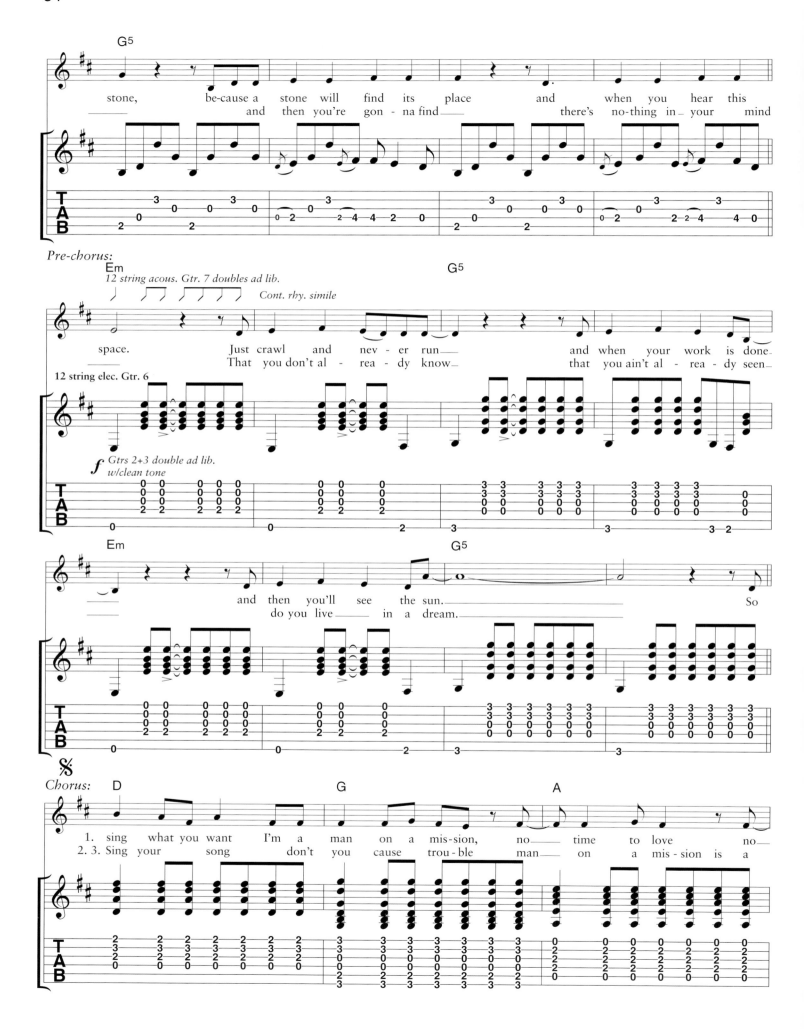

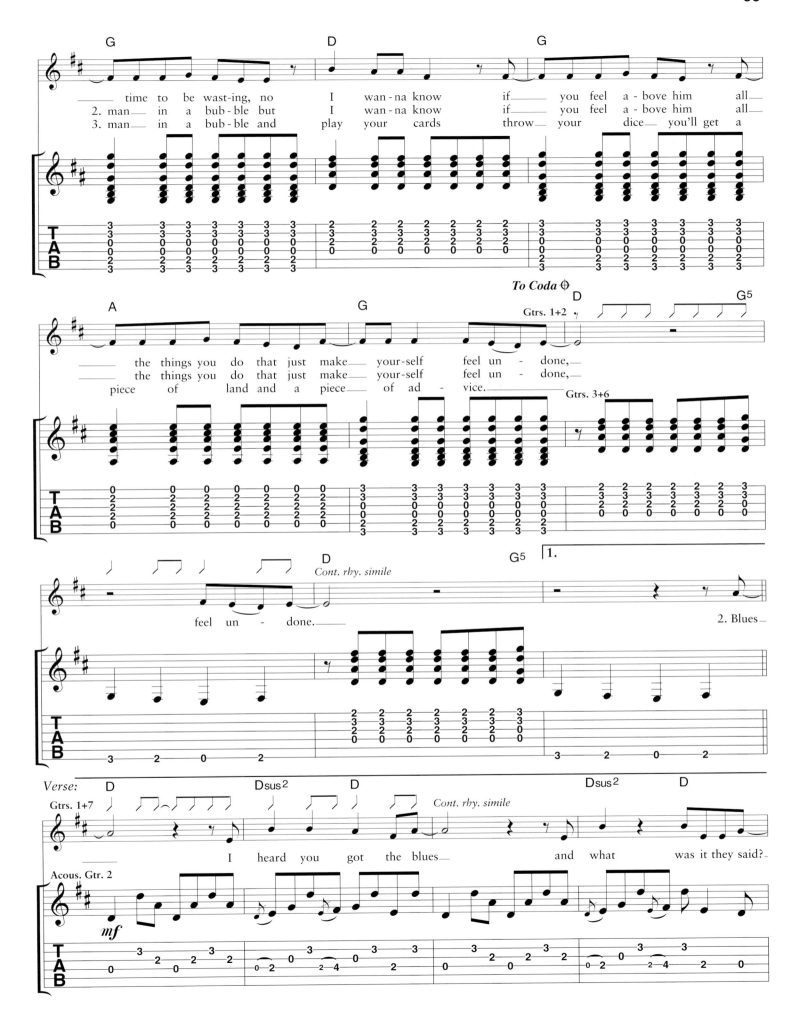

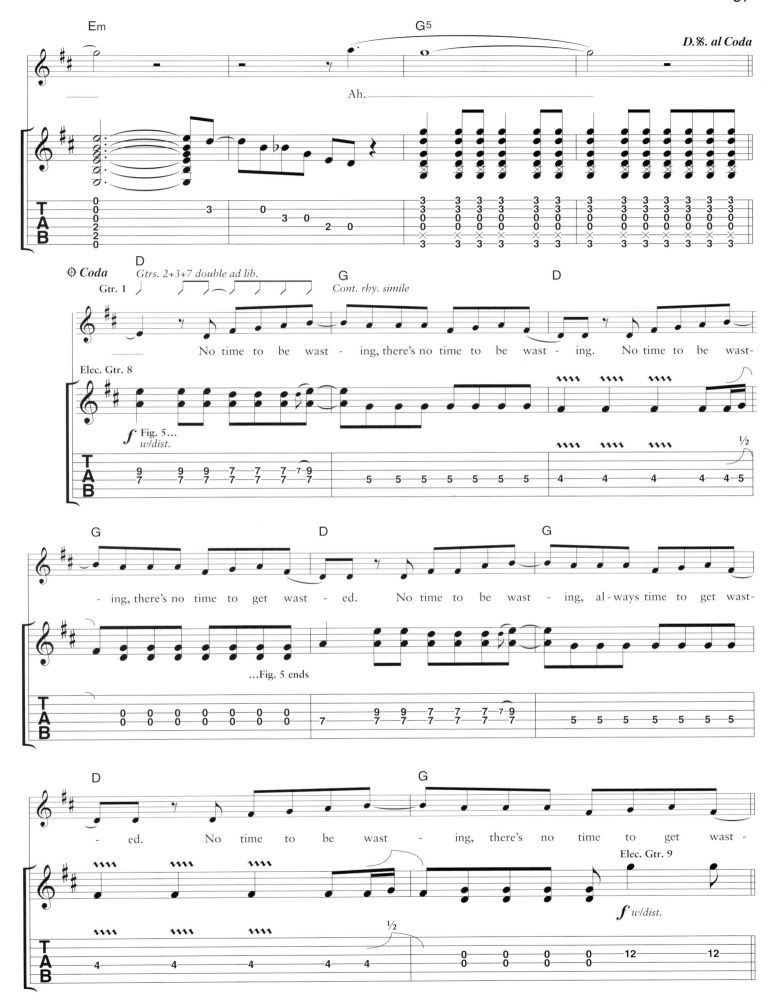

Will Malone

Talvin Singh

Chris Potter

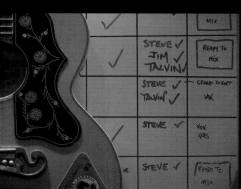

STEVE ✓
JIM ✓
TALVIN ✓

STEVE ✓
TALVIN ✓

STEVE ✓

STEVE ✓

MIX

READY TO MIX

GEONE TO SORT: VOX

VOX GTRS

READY TO MIX

Running Away

Words and Music by Richard Ashcroft

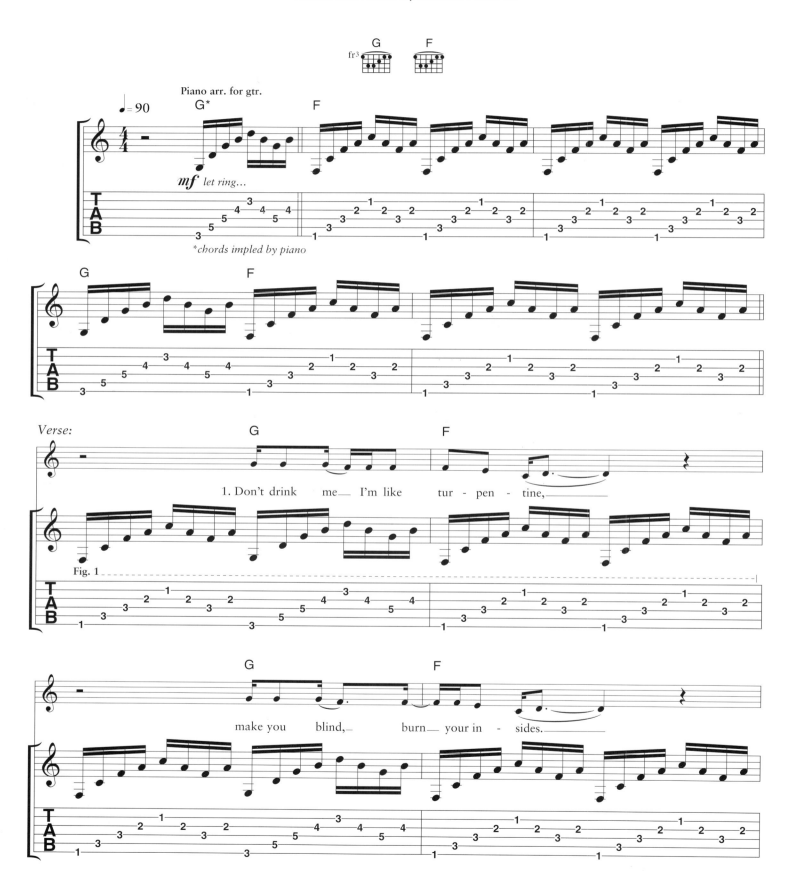

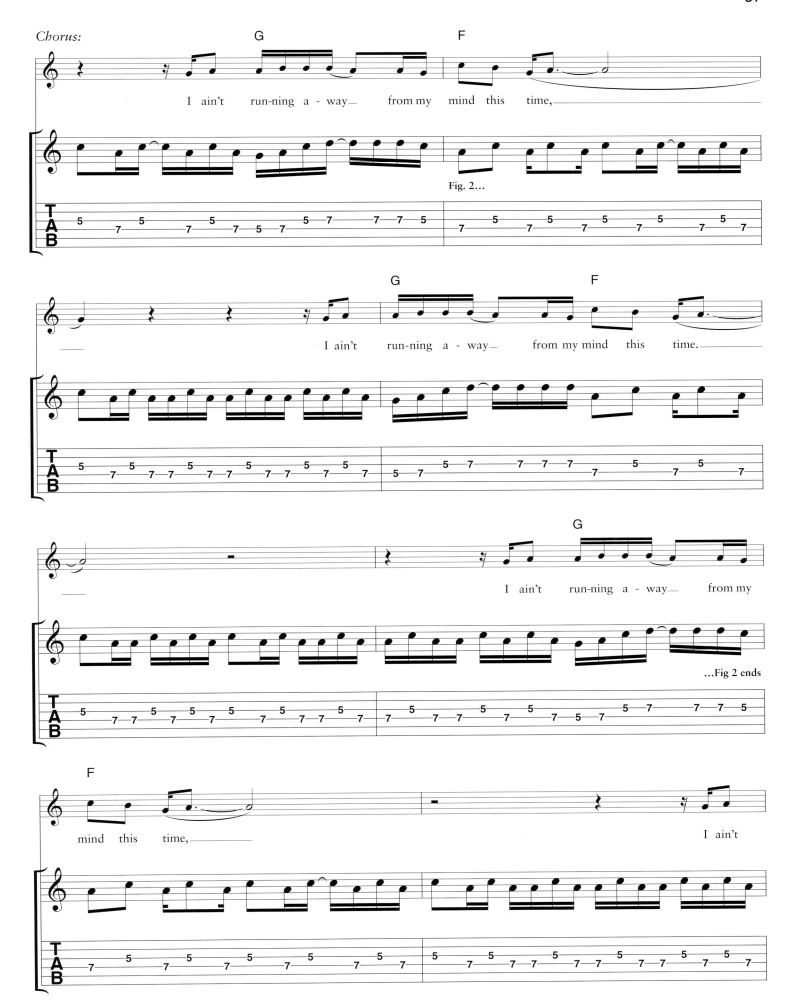

Lord I've Been Trying

Words and Music by Richard Ashcroft

Nature Is The Law

Words and Music by Richard Ashcroft

The Miracle

Words and Music by Richard Ashcroft

Don't drink me

Some are living and some are dead

and some are hiding, waiting for the sun